LEMON DROP BOOKS

www.lemondropbooks.co.uk

First paperback edition printed 2018 United Kingdom

A catalogue record for this book is available from the British Library

ISBN 978-0-9935031-4-6

Published by Lemon Drop Books

Printed in Great Britain

THE MAGICAL WOOD

By Mark Lemon
Illustrated by Maia Walczak

Published by Lemon Drop Books

This is a story about the tree family.

The trees live in the magical wood with their friends, the animals.

You know the type of trees: strong and tall with beautiful green leaves flowing down from their branches. These magical trees were protected by the two oldest trees, Strongest Tree and Guardian Tree.

Wandering through the magical wood ran a long, winding river that flowed down to the sea. The animals loved to play in the river. In the summertime, they enjoyed splashing about and having lots of fun in the water. It was a happy place to be.

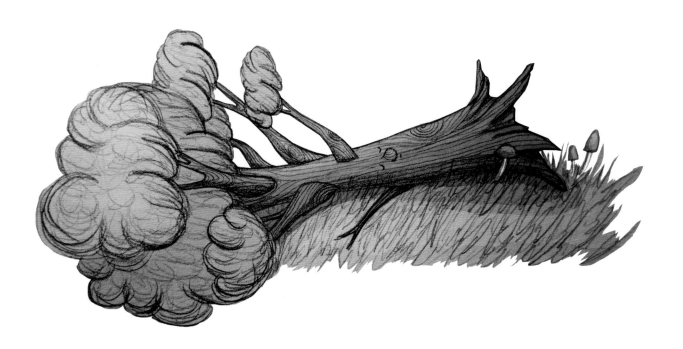

One cold and stormy day, the wind blew a terrible gale.
The animals were frightened and took shelter from the storm in their homes.

In the morning, the tree family woke to a sad sight.
Strongest Tree was lying on the woodland floor. It had died in the night.

All of the animals gathered, around their fallen friend.
Rivers of tears flowed, as if water gushing out to sea.

The tree family had changed forever, the life that they once knew, now was no more.

This page is for you.

IT'S
okay to
FEEL SAD.

Guardian Tree was sad, the magical wood has lost their friend.

"How will we survive the seasons?" it thought.

When summer arrived, the morning sun shone through the leaves.

An old friend came to visit. It was Mr. Bear with a gift for Guardian Tree.

"Good morning, Guardian Tree," said Mr. Bear.

"I am here to give you some hope.

These words that I will say to you,

Will surely help you to cope."

"At the start, you'll have a sad heart,

But this pain you feel will ease,

This is what happens when someone grieves."

Mr. Bear left Guardian Tree, bidding the magical wood farewell.
The season had changed to autumn; the leaves had fallen to the ground.
Guardian Tree had a new visitor. Mrs. Owl had flown in.

"Good evening, Guardian Tree," said Mrs. Owl.
"I have some special words for you,"

"These feelings you have are painful,
But you will feel better I know.
The feelings you have are like a river,
It will always flow."

CLOSE YOUR EYES AND remember someone SPECIAL.

This page is for you.

Mrs. Owl left Guardian Tree, bidding them goodnight.

As the season had changed to winter, snow had covered the wood in a beautiful white powder. The wood was now quiet and all of the animals were hibernating in their homes.

Guardian Tree had another visitor. Mr. Robin, the winter bird.

"Good morning, Guardian Tree," said Mr. Robin.
"I am here to check if you're okay?"
"I have some words to help you,
Through this cold winter day."
"Sometimes people leave,
But they are always in your heart.
If you close your eyes and remember,
You will never be apart."

Mr. Robin left Guardian Tree, returning to the wood.

Springtime had now arrived, the leaves on the trees had begun to grow.

Guardian Tree had one final visitor. Mrs. Rabbit with a message for the trees:

"Good morning, Guardian Tree, " said Mrs. Rabbit.
I am here to support the trees.
I would like to give you these special words,
To help your pain ease."
"When someone special dies,
It's always hard to believe.
Please remember when I tell you,
They're with you in the breeze through the leaves."

Mrs. Rabbit left Guardian Tree, hopping back to her burrow.

Surprised, Guardian Tree looked down to see a wonderful sight;

Beautiful flowers had grown where Strongest Tree once stood.

Their friends from the magical wood supported them through this sad time.

Through the seasons, the trees slowly started to feel better, but they will always miss their friend.

So, please remember this story, if a special person dies.

They will always be in your heart, remember them when you close your eyes.

WINSTON'S WISH WW

Giving hope to grieving children

WINSTON'S WISH SUPPORTS BEREAVED CHILDREN AND THEIR FAMILIES AFTER THE DEATH OF A PARENT OR SIBLING

FREEPHONE NATIONAL HELPLINE

Parents, carers and professionals can call our National Helpline for free on **08088 020 021** for ongoing support and advice, Monday – Friday, 9am – 5.30pm. *Please visit the website for current opening hours.*

ONLINE

For parents and professionals, visit **winstonswish.org** For young people, visit **help2makesense.org**

TRAINING

Professionals can access our training to give them the tools needed to support bereaved children and families. Visit **winstonswish.org/training**

PUBLICATIONS & RESOURCES

We have a range of publications and resources aimed at helping bereaved children come to terms with their grief. Visit **shop.winstonswish.org**

OTHER SUPPORT AVAILABLE

Childhood Bereavement Network
Provides a directory of organisations around the country that can offer local bereavement services to families and young people. Also offers publications, information and training.
Phone: **020 7843 6309** Email: **cbn@ncb.org.uk**
www.childhoodbereavementnetwork.org.uk

Professional Association for Childcare and Early Years (PACEY)
PACEY is a membership organisation for childminders and other individual child carers also produces guides to supporting children through bereavement and trauma more generally.
Phone: **0300 003 0005** Email: **info@pacey.org.uk**
www.pacey.org.uk

Pre-school Learning Alliance
The Pre-school Learning Alliance a membership organisation for childcare providers, offering advice and support for people working with young children.
Phone: **020 7697 2500** Email: **info@pre-school.org.uk**
www.pre-school.org.uk

National Day Nurseries Association (NDNA)
A national charity which aims to share good practice and ideas with childcare providers to make sure that children get the best possible start in life.
Phone: **01484 40 70 70**
www.ndna.org.uk

Giving hope to grieving children

Winston's Wish is a Registered Charity (England and Wales) 1061359, (Scotland) SC041140 | 0201

These are the stairs to heaven

balloons we send off to grampy

me grampy

Angel grampy

I'm Happy here because I'm thinking of happy times

Here I'm Sad because I'm missing grampy and worried about my mum being sad.

Charlie Reid - 8yrs
Ilminster Avenue E-Act Academy

ACKNOWLEDGEMENTS

Thank you to Winston's Wish for advising me on this very special project.

It wouldn't have been possible to bring this story to life, if it wasn't for the amazing Illustrations by Maia Walczak.

Big thanks to Lucy Fey NLP & Hypnotherapy Bristol and all the proof readers for casting their talented eyes over the story.

The final product wouldn't have been possible if it wasn't for Doveton Press Printers, Bristol.

Finally, I would like to thank my family – Simone you have been a continued support whilst I have been through this process, I love you very much! And Otis and Thea for the continued inspiration to create new stories.

Very special dedication to Dad - James Lemon
'You walk with me always'